HSC
Health & Safety Commission

The control of asbestos at work (Third edition)

Control of Asbestos at Work Regulations 1987

APPROVED CODE OF PRACTICE

L27

HSE BOOKS

The Approved Code of Practice

This Code has been approved by the Health and Safety
Commission, with the consent of the Secretary of State.
It gives practical advice on how to comply with the law.
If you follow the advice you will be doing enough to comply
with the law in respect of those specific matters on which the
Code gives advice. You may use alternative methods to those
set out in the Code in order to comply with the law.

However, the Code has special legal status. If you are
prosecuted for breach of health and safety law, and it is
proved that you did not follow the relevant provisions of
the Code, you will need to show that you have complied
with the law in some other way or a court will find you at fault.

Contents

Notice of Approval

By virtue of section 16(4) of the Health and Safety at Work etc Act 1974 and with the consent of the Secretary of State for the Environment, Transport and the Regions, the Health and Safety Commission has on 3 November 1999 approved the revision of the Code of Practice now entitled *The control of asbestos at work (Third edition)*.

The Code of Practice gives practical guidance on the Control of Asbestos at Work Regulations 1987 as amended by the Control of Asbestos at Work (Amendment) Regulations 1992 and the Control of Asbestos at Work (Amendment) Regulations 1998.

The Code of Practice comes into effect on 1 February 1999 which is the date when the Control of Asbestos at Work (Amendment) Regulations 1998 come into force. On that date, the edition which came into force on 1 January 1993 shall cease to have effect.

Signed

ROSEMARY BANNER
Secretary to the Health and Safety Commission

6 January 1999

Application

This Approved Code of Practice (ACOP) applies to most work with asbestos. It applies to work with asbestos during manufacturing processes, work on building materials which contain asbestos, asbestos sampling and laboratory analysis.

The only work with asbestos which is not covered by this ACOP is work which involves clearing asbestos-contaminated land, asbestos insulation, asbestos coating and asbestos insulating board, where either:

(a)   any person who carries out the work spends more than a total of 1 hour in any seven days; or

(b)   the total time spent on the work by all the people working on it exceeds 2 hours.

Such work requires a licence from HSE under regulation 3 of the Asbestos (Licensing) Regulations 1983 (ASLIC)[1] unless it is work carried on by employers with their own workers at their own premises. In either case the ACOP *Work with asbestos insulation, asbestos coating and asbestos insulating board*[2] applies.

Part I of this ACOP gives general advice on complying with the Control of Asbestos at Work Regulations 1987 (CAW) and is applicable to *both* manufacturing processes and building work. Part II gives additional advice specific to the manufacturing industry and Part III gives additional advice specific to those working on asbestos-containing building materials in the course of building and maintenance work such as plumbing and electrical installation.

Although only a court can give an authoritative interpretation of the law, in considering the application of this ACOP and guidance to people under your control and direction who are self-employed for tax and/or National Insurance purposes, they are likely to be treated as your employees for health and safety purposes. You may therefore need to take appropriate action to protect them. If you are in any doubt about who is responsible for the health and safety of a person working for you this could be clarified and included in the terms of a contract. However, remember you cannot pass on a legal duty that falls to you under the Health and Safety at Work etc Act 1974 (HSW Act)[3] by means of a contract and you will still retain duties towards others by virtue of section 3 of the HSW Act. If you intend to employ such workers on the basis that you are not responsible for their health and safety, you should seek legal advice before doing so.

Meaning of 'reasonably practicable'

The term 'so far as is reasonably practicable' appears often in this guidance and means that the degree of risk in a particular job or workplace needs to be balanced against the time, trouble, cost, benefit and physical difficulty of taking measures to avoid or reduce the risk. However, it should not be used as an excuse to avoid taking safety measures, and if unsure you should err on the side of caution.

THE APPROVED CODE OF PRACTICE

Part I General advice on complying with the Control of Asbestos at Work Regulations

Introduction

1   Most of the duties in the Control of Asbestos at Work Regulations are placed upon 'an employer', that is, the person who employs the workers who are liable to be exposed to asbestos in the course of their work. Although the Regulations always refer to an employer, regulation 3 makes it clear that self-employed people have the same duties towards themselves and others as an employer has towards his or her employees and others.

2   Where work with asbestos forms part of a larger project there will be a particular need to co-operate with other employers, and there may be other regulations which must be taken into account. However, the responsibility to ensure compliance with the provisions of the Control of Asbestos at Work Regulations remains with the employer or self-employed person described in paragraph 1.

Regulation 2

The action levels and control limits

3   In general, the Regulations apply to any exposure to asbestos at work, but some particular regulations are triggered only if exposure is liable to exceed an action level. The action levels are exposures to asbestos accumulated over a continuous 12-week period, and expressed as fibre-hours per millilitre of air (fibre-hours/ml). If, from the assessment of the work (see regulation 5), it is likely that the exposure of any employee will exceed 72 fibre-hours/ml for chrysotile or 48 fibre-hours/ml for all other forms of asbestos, either alone or in mixtures, including mixtures containing chrysotile, then the action level will be exceeded.

4   When the action level is exceeded then the regulations on notification of the work, designated areas and medical surveillance will apply (regulations 6, 14 and 16 respectively).

5   Like the action level, the control limits for asbestos also trigger particular regulations. If, from the assessment of the work required by regulation 5, it is concluded that the exposure of an employee is liable to exceed a control limit, the employer must provide suitable respiratory protective equipment (see regulation 8(2)). The control limits also trigger the need for respirator zones which are required under regulation 14.

6   To decide whether or not the action level and/or the control limits are likely to be exceeded, you need to know what the concentration of asbestos fibres in the air in the workplace is likely to be. This can be estimated using information about the type of asbestos and the sort of work intended, or by past experience of that sort of work. Where there is doubt it will be necessary to confirm the estimated exposures by measurement, using a method approved by the Health and Safety Commission (HSC). Guidance on methods approved by HSC may be found in the following publications *Asbestos: exposure limits and measurements of airborne dust concentrations*[4] and *Asbestos fibres in air: sampling and evaluation by phase contrast microscopy (PCM) under the Control of Asbestos at Work Regulations.*[5]

Regulation 3

ACOP

3

Duties relating to people other than the employer's own employees

7   Employers must take into account people other than their own employees in the assessment required by regulation 5 and in the action taken to prevent or control exposure required by regulation 8.

8   Where two or more employers work with asbestos at the same time at the same workplace they should co-operate in order to meet their separate responsibilities under these Regulations.

Regulation 4

ACOP

4

Identification of the type of asbestos

9   Regulation 4 gives employers the choice of either:

(a)   identifying the sort of asbestos their workers could come into contact with before the job starts; or

(b)   assuming that any asbestos present is amphibole asbestos, and working out their assessment and plan of work on that basis.

10   Employers must decide whether it is practicable to avoid exposure to asbestos altogether. In the manufacturing industry this must be by using a substitute material wherever practicable. It is more difficult in building and maintenance work, but employers should consider whether it is possible to do the work in some way that avoids contact with asbestos.

Regulations 5 and 5A

ACOP

5 and 5A

The assessment and plan of work

11   If asbestos has to be used, or work which is liable to expose employees to asbestos is unavoidable, employers must carry out an adequate assessment of the likely exposure of employees and others who may be affected by the work. Employers may also have duties under other regulations to carry out a separate risk assessment; for instance if employees are likely to be exposed to other hazardous substances an assessment will be required under the Control of Substances Hazardous to Health Regulations (COSHH) 1994.[6] Employers should make sure that assessments are carried out by a competent person. To be competent, the person should have had adequate information, instruction and training in accordance with regulation 7 and have adequate knowledge of the type of work and of available control measures.

12   Where the work is straightforward and expected to produce airborne fibre levels so low that the assessment is simple, a generic form of assessment may be used.

13   To be adequate, the assessment should cover:

(a)   a description of the work and expected duration;

(b)   a note of either the type of asbestos and the results of any analysis, or the assumption that the asbestos is not chrysotile alone so that the stricter action levels and control limits apply, and a description of the quantity and condition of the asbestos-containing material;

(c)   the controls to be applied to prevent or control exposure, including, where appropriate, the provision of personal protective equipment (PPE);

(d)   the reasons for the chosen work method;

(e)   details of expected exposures, noting:

  (i)   whether they are liable to exceed the action level and or the control limit and the number of people affected;

  (ii)   if it is known that exposure will be above either of the relevant control limits, the expected exposure, so that appropriate respiratory protective equipment (RPE) can be selected;

  (iii)   if exposures are intermittent, the frequency and duration of exposures;

  (iv)   whether anyone other than employees may be exposed, and their expected exposure;

  (v)   where applicable, results already available from air monitoring of similar work;

(f)   the steps to be taken to reduce exposure to the lowest level reasonably practicable;

(g)   the steps to be taken to reduce the release of asbestos to the environment;

(h)   where applicable, procedures for provision and use of RPE and any other PPE;

(i)   where appropriate, procedures for dealing with emergencies;

(j)   procedures for the removal of waste from the workplace;

(k)   any other information relevant to safe working practices.

Reviewing the assessment

14   Where monitoring of exposure levels, or other information gathered during the course of work, suggests that the initial assessment was wrong in respect of either the duration of the task or the nature of the materials concerned, consideration should immediately be given to whether the ACOP *Work with asbestos insulation, asbestos coating and asbestos insulating board* applies, and if it does the guidance in that ACOP should be followed.

15   In circumstances other than those in paragraph 14, employers should review assessments whenever there is reason to suspect they are no longer valid, particularly if:

(a)   fibre control methods change;

(b)   there is doubt about the efficiency of control measures;

(c)   there is a significant change in the type of work or method of work; or

5

(d) technological or scientific advances allow for more efficient control methods.

16 In addition to reviews triggered by the changes mentioned in paragraph 15, the assessment should be reviewed at regular intervals if the type of work is long term. The assessment should be reviewed at between two- and five-year intervals and should note when the next planned review is due to be carried out. Similarly, control measures should be re-examined to assess whether exposures can be reduced still further.

17 A copy of the assessment must be kept readily available on site and should be brought to the attention of anyone carrying out visual inspection and air clearance monitoring.

Regulation 6

When to notify

18 For work which does not require a licence from the Health and Safety Executive (HSE), the duty to notify the enforcing authority applies only on the first occasion when work with asbestos is liable to result in employees' exposure exceeding the appropriate action level. This might be the very first job that an employer carries out, or it could be one of a number of consecutive jobs which triggers the notification requirement because the action level relates to cumulative exposures over a continuous 12-week period. The only exception to this general rule is where subsequent work would be materially different from that normally carried out and described in the first notification. In such instances, employers must submit a separate notification.

Regulation 7

Information, instruction and training

19 Information, instruction and training given to employees, including supervisors, should cover, in appropriate detail, both by written and oral presentation as well as by demonstration:

(a) the health hazards of asbestos, including the health risks to employees' families and others which could result from taking home asbestos-contaminated equipment and clothing and the dramatically increased risk of lung cancer for asbestos workers who also smoke;

(b) how controls, protective equipment and work methods can reduce those risks;

(c) the uses and likely occurrence of asbestos in buildings and plant;

(d) the assessment of exposure and the purpose of air monitoring;

(e) the control limits and action levels and their meaning;

(f) work methods and the correct use of control measures to limit the spread of asbestos fibres outside the work area, and to limit the exposures to workers inside the work area to as low as is reasonably practicable;

(g) why the particular control methods used were chosen to reduce dust emission;

(h) the maintenance of control measures, including the maintenance of enclosures and negative pressure equipment;

(i) procedures for reporting and correcting defects;

(j) the correct selection from a range of suitable RPE, its correct use, cleaning, maintenance and safe storage, with specific attention to ensuring that the RPE is working correctly in accordance with the manufacturer's instruction and information, and, checking the fit of face masks to ensure a good seal is achieved;

(k) the correct use, storage and maintenance of protective clothing;

(l) decontamination procedures;

(m) the general procedures to be followed to deal with an emergency, eg an uncontrolled release of asbestos dust into the workplace;

(n) waste disposal;

(o) the role of medical surveillance;

(p) record-keeping, eg records of examinations of control measures.

20 Anyone who carries out any examination, testing (including clearance inspection, air monitoring and exposure monitoring) or maintenance of plant or equipment should be suitably trained.

21 Training for safety representatives and employee representatives will need to be appropriate to their role. More information on training can be found in HSE guidance *Training operatives and supervisors for work with asbestos insulation and coatings*.[7]

Refresher training

22 Refresher training covering the topics in paragraphs 19-21 should be given at least every year, or more frequently if necessary, particularly if:

(a) work methods change;

(b) the type of equipment used to control exposure changes; or

(c) the type of work carried out changes significantly.

23 Additional training and refresher training may be required for people carrying out specific tasks. For example, people carrying out examinations and tests on local exhaust ventilation (LEV) systems and RPE should have had sufficient training and experience in inspection methods and techniques to ensure that they are competent, and people responsible for maintenance of plant or equipment will need training (including refresher training) in those tasks.

24 All training should be provided by somebody who is competent to provide it and has had adequate personal practical experience and theoretical knowledge of all relevant aspects of the work being carried out by the employer.

Information and training of non-employees

25 Employers have a duty under regulation 3(1)(a) of the Control of Asbestos at Work Regulations to ensure, so far as is reasonably practicable, that adequate information, instruction and training are given to non-employees who are on the premises and could be affected by the work, as well as to their own employees. Information, instruction and training will need to take

ACOP

account of any possible risks resulting from rearrangement of thoroughfares and fire exits as well as the risks arising from disturbance of asbestos-containing materials.

26   Training procedures, including those for refresher training, should be set out in writing.

Availability of information

27   Employers should make the following information available, on request, to employees, employee representatives and to safety representatives:

(a)   a copy of the current assessment for the workplace;

(b)   details of any air monitoring strategy and any results;

(c)   maintenance records for control measures;

(d)   details of any notification to the enforcing authority under regulation 6 concerning that workplace;

(e)   any **anonymous** collective information from the health records; and

(f)   personal information from health records (**only to the individual employees concerned**).

28   Where the results of air monitoring show that the relevant control limit has been unexpectedly exceeded, employers should tell employees and safety representatives about this as quickly as possible and give details of the reasons for what happened and the action taken or proposed.

Procedures for providing information, instruction and training

29   There should be a written statement setting out procedures for providing information, instruction and training. This should be reviewed regularly, particularly when work methods change.

30   Employers should consult safety representatives and employee representatives in good time about the information, instruction and training which they intend to provide.

7

Regulation 8

Preventing and controlling exposure

ACOP

31   Prevention of exposure must be the employer's first objective. Where it is not reasonably practicable to prevent exposure, employers must reduce it to the lowest concentration reasonably practicable by means other than the use of RPE. This means keeping the level of fibres released into the air to an absolute minimum during work with asbestos.

32   In devising systems to do this, employers must consult safety representatives appointed by recognised trade unions under the Safety Representatives and Safety Committees Regulations 1977.[8] Employees not covered by such representatives must be consulted, either directly or indirectly via elected representatives of employee safety, according to the Health and Safety (Consultation with Employees) Regulations 1996.[9] Such consultations allow employees or their representatives to help employers develop control measures.

8

Respiratory protective equipment

33   If, despite the use of other control measures, exposures still have the potential to exceed the control limits, employers must provide suitable RPE and make sure that it is used correctly by those carrying out the work. Employers must choose RPE which is designed to provide an adequate margin of safety. To be suitable, RPE must be matched to the job, the environment, the anticipated maximum exposure and to the wearer. It must reduce the concentration of asbestos fibres inhaled to a concentration as low as is reasonably practicable and in any case to a level which is below the control limits. This means that even if the control limit is achieved, it is necessary to reduce exposures still further where it is reasonably practicable to do so.

Quantitative face-fit testing

34   The performance of a tight-fitting facepiece (filtering facepieces, half and full face masks) depends on a good contact between the wearer's skin and the face seal of the mask. **It should be noted that a good face seal can only be achieved for this type of RPE if the wearer is clean shaven.** To make sure that the selected RPE can provide adequate protection for the wearer, the initial selection should include quantitative fit testing.

35   This fit test could be undertaken in two ways:

(a)   it can be carried out in an enclosure into which it is possible to deliver, measure and maintain standard aerosols of sodium chloride or sulphur hexafluoride gas; or

(b)   it can be carried out using an ambient particulate counting device. This device uses ambient aerosol to perform the fit testing and it should be used in accordance with the manufacturer's instructions by a trained operative.

36   Repeat quantitative face-fit testing will be needed if it is decided to change to a different model of RPE or different sized facepiece or if there have been significant changes to the facial characteristics of the wearer, for example as a result of significant weight gain or loss or dentistry. Repeat testing will not be required following a change of employer, provided that the same type of RPE continues to be used by the worker.

Uncontrolled releases

37   If, in spite of the control measures, there is an accidental uncontrolled release of asbestos into the workplace at a concentration that is likely to exceed any control limit, then measures, including emergency procedures, must be in place to limit exposure and the risks to health. The cause of the uncontrolled release should be identified and adequate control regained as soon as possible.

38   Employers should make sure the contaminated area is thoroughly cleaned of visible debris or dust that may have become contaminated by asbestos fibres. Employees doing this work should wear appropriate PPE, including RPE. It is essential that a careful check is undertaken to ensure that this work has been properly carried out. Air sampling should then be carried out to confirm that the remedial measures taken have been effective.

39   Only those people who are essential in carrying out repairs and other necessary cleaning and maintenance work should be allowed into the affected area. A note that the exposure has occurred should be added to the employee's exposure record (see paragraph 73) or to the employee's personnel record if they do not have an exposure record. A copy of the note should be given to the employee with instructions that it should be kept indefinitely.

Regulation 9   Use of control measures

40   Employers should have procedures in place to make sure that control measures are properly used or applied and are not made less effective by other work practices or other machinery. These procedures should include:

(a)   checks at the start of every shift and the end of each day; and

(b)   prompt action when a problem is identified.

General duties on employees

41   Within the general duties imposed by regulation 9(2), employees should, in particular:

(a)   use any control measures, including RPE and protective clothing, properly and keep it in the places provided;

(b)   follow carefully all the procedures set out in the employer's assessment and plan of work (see paragraphs 12 and 13), including those for changing and decontamination;

(c)   keep the workplace clean;

(d)   eat, drink and smoke only in the places provided.

Use of RPE and protective clothing

42   Respirators should never be hung around the neck in contact with contaminated clothing, or put down or stored in a contaminated area.

43   RPE and protective clothing should be removed at the end of the working period, cleaned (paragraph 46 for RPE, paragraph 56 for PPE) and then placed in storage provided specifically for that purpose. Disposable RPE and protective clothing should be treated as asbestos waste.

44   RPE should never be taken off and put down in a contaminated area, except in the case of a medical emergency. When not in use, RPE should not be hung around the neck or in any other way be allowed to come into contact with contaminated clothing. When not in use, RPE should be stored in a place which is clean, will protect it from damage and is specifically provided for that purpose.

9

Regulation 10   Maintenance and testing of respiratory protective equipment

45   When RPE is routinely used, employers should make sure it is always examined before it is put on - to check that it is in good working order. The pre-use examination should include checks on:

(a)   the condition of the head harness and facepiece including seal and visor;

(b)   the condition of inhalation and exhalation valves, if fitted;

(c)   the type and condition of the filter;

10

(d)   the battery charge/condition;

(e)   airflow rate for powered respirators; and

(f)   additional tests in accordance with the manufacturer's instructions.

46   RPE needs to be inspected and cleaned after each use and, additionally, disinfected whenever the equipment is transferred from one person to another. Maintenance and cleaning procedures need to be suitable for the type of RPE being used and should be based on the manufacturer's cleaning and maintenance schedules.

47   All RPE should be thoroughly examined and tested at least once every month to make sure that it is working properly to its design specification.

People competent to test RPE

48   Those people carrying out examinations and tests on RPE should be competent and have adequate knowledge, training and experience in examination methods and techniques.

Other equipment and controls

49   Employers should make sure that maintenance procedures are drawn up for all control measures and PPE, including cleaning equipment, washing and changing facilities and controls, to prevent the spread of contamination. The procedures should make clear:

(a)   what control measures require maintenance;

(b)   when and how the maintenance is to be carried out; and

(c)   who is responsible for maintenance and making good any defects.

Records of examination and test

50   Employers must keep a record of any examinations and tests carried out on control measures for at least five years.

10

Regulation 11   ## Provision of protective clothing

51   As part of the assessment required by regulation 5, the employer must decide whether or not protective clothing is required for work with asbestos. The assessment should start from the assumption that protective clothing will be necessary unless exposures are extremely slight and infrequent.

Adequacy and suitability of protective clothing

52   Protective clothing should be worn whenever asbestos is likely to be deposited on clothing. In general, the protective clothing should be appropriate and suitable to the job and must protect the parts of the body likely to be affected. It may range from a dust jacket for low infrequent exposures to full PPE where a significant amount of asbestos contamination is likely to occur. Employers will need to take into account the likely exposure to decide what sort of PPE, including RPE, they need to provide. If the work involves exposure that exceeds the appropriate control limit, a full set of protective clothing, including headwear and appropriate footwear, will always be necessary.

11

53   To be adequate and suitable, PPE should:

(a)   fit the wearer. It needs to be of sufficient size to avoid straining and ripping the joints, comfortable, and where appropriate allow for heat and physical stress, and suitable for cold environments, and for possible contact with hot surfaces;

(b)   prevent penetration by asbestos fibres;

(c)   be designed to fit closely at the neck, wrists and ankles;

(d)   not have pockets or other attachments which could trap asbestos dust; and

(e)   be easily decontaminated.

54   Where full PPE is provided, the headcovering should be close-fitting, covering the parts of the head and neck not covered by the facepiece of the respirator. The headcovering should be connected to the main overall, and headstraps of RPE should be worn under the headcovering.

Use of protective equipment

55   Protective clothing should be removed before taking off RPE and before leaving the working area for any reason, including meal breaks, other breaks and at the end of the shift. Protective clothing should be vacuum-cleaned before removal using a type H (BS 5415)[10] vacuum cleaner fitted with suitable attachments. Once removed, it should be placed in the storage area specifically provided for that purpose and at a safe distance from changing facilities; or sealed in a dust-tight bag if it is to be removed from the premises for cleaning, or for disposal as asbestos waste. It must never be taken home.

Cleaning of protective equipment

56   Non-disposable protective clothing must be washed at suitable intervals. It may be cleaned by the employer if they have suitably equipped premises or sent to a laundry which has the facilities and expertise to launder asbestos-contaminated clothing safely. Clothing for despatch to a laundry should be placed in dust-tight hot-water soluble bags which can then be loaded unopened into a washing machine. These inner bags should then be placed inside a second bag which is labelled in accordance with regulation 18. The bags should be strong enough to remain dust-tight during transit and handling. Employers must make sure that protective clothing is removed at the end of a working period and placed in storage provided specifically for that purpose.

57   All premises where contaminated clothing is cleaned should be equipped with an integrated washing/drying machine and be fitted with a high-efficiency particulate arrester (HEPA) air filtration unit to remove asbestos from the air vented during drying before it is discharged either into the atmosphere or into the premises.

Regulation 12   **Preventing the spread of asbestos**

58   Any plant or equipment which has been contaminated with asbestos should be thoroughly decontaminated before it is moved for use in other premises or for disposal. Asbestos materials should never be left loose or in a state where they can be trampled or otherwise spread.

Regulation 14 — Asbestos areas and respirator zones

59   The purpose of marking asbestos areas is to help prevent or reduce exposure and the spread of contamination by making sure that workers do not enter areas where they may be exposed to significant concentrations of asbestos unknowingly (such that the action level would be exceeded if the workers spent their normal work time exposed to that concentration of asbestos). The purpose of marking areas as respirator zones is to ensure that RPE is worn whenever the control limits are liable to be exceeded.

60   Because of the differences between the action level and the control limit, it is possible for an area to be designated as:

(a)   a respirator zone (because either of the relevant control limits is liable to be exceeded), but not as an asbestos area (because the action level is not liable to be exceeded); or

(b)   an asbestos area, but not a respirator zone; or

(c)   a respirator zone and an asbestos area.

61   Employers must make sure that employees do not eat, drink, or smoke in any areas which have been marked as asbestos areas or respirator zones. Employers must provide suitable facilities outside the working area where employees can eat, drink, etc. The facilities should be conveniently accessible to workers and to washing facilities and suitable toilet facilities, and users should wash before eating or drinking, etc in order to reduce the risk of breathing in asbestos fibres.

14

Regulation 15 — Monitoring

When monitoring is appropriate

62   Monitoring of employee exposure consists of personal sampling followed by analysis using a method approved by HSC. Its main purpose is to protect the health of employees by determining or checking the concentrations of airborne asbestos to which they are exposed. Information on employee exposure needs to be compared with the action levels and control limits as the results may trigger the need for certain control measures.

63   Monitoring will be appropriate unless:

(a)   exposures are known to be low and not likely to approach the relevant control limits and/or action levels;

(b)   the work is intermittent and of short duration and adequate information is available to enable the appropriate protective equipment to be provided; and

(c)   the protective equipment provided is of such a standard that no foreseeable measurement result could indicate a need for equipment of a higher standard.

64   If the employer decides monitoring is not necessary then he or she should use other sources of information about the likely concentrations of asbestos in the air, for instance guidance as issued by HSE in HSG173[11] or previous experience of the work.

15

65   Monitoring should always be done when there are any doubts about the effectiveness of the measures taken to reduce the concentration of asbestos in air, and in particular to reduce that concentration below the relevant control limit. Monitoring is appropriate therefore:

(a)   to check the effectiveness of control measures, ie that engineering controls are working as they should to their design specification and do not need repair; and

(b)   to confirm that the RPE chosen provides the appropriate degree of protection where exposure exceeds, or is liable to exceed, the control limit.

66   Monitoring of employee exposure should be by personal sampling. Static sampling can be used to check that control measures are effective.

67   In continuous or repetitive processes, routine monitoring should be carried out at least once every three months, although the frequency may be reduced to once a year where:

(a)   there is no substantial change in workplace conditions; and

(b)   the results of the two preceding measurements have not exceeded half the relevant control limit.

68   Where groups of workers are doing the same type of work in similar conditions, sampling can be carried out on a group basis. Individuals chosen for sampling within a group should be selected at random.

69   Employers should consult employees, safety representatives or employee representatives when making arrangements for monitoring. Further guidance on when air monitoring is necessary is given in HSG173 *Monitoring strategies for toxic substances.*[11]

Adequacy of monitoring procedures

70   Employers wishing to engage laboratories to carry out air monitoring must only engage those laboratories which can demonstrate they conform with EN 45001[12] by accreditation with a recognised accreditation body. Employers carrying out their own air monitoring should make sure that the employees carrying out this monitoring receive a similar standard of training, supervision and quality control to those required by EN 45001.

71   All records of monitoring should state the employer's name and address, the site address where appropriate, the date, and should include:

(a)   the type of work being carried out and, where relevant, its exact location;

(b)   the type of sample, ie personal, static, clearance, etc;

(c)   the location of any static sampler;

(d)   the date and time of sampling, sample duration and the flow rate;

(e)   the length of time for which individuals are exposed;

(f)   the measured fibre concentration;

(g)   the fibre type if known; and

(h)   the names of the sampler and analyst or the names of their organisations.

72   Where employees are under medical surveillance (see regulation 16), it will be necessary to retain a summary of any air monitoring results (or the original results themselves) to supplement the health record (see paragraphs 70 and 71). Any summary of air monitoring results should contain enough information about airborne fibre concentrations to allow individual average exposures for different types of work to be calculated as accurately as possible. The summary, or the original results, should be kept for the same length of time as the health record, ie 40 years. Further guidance on monitoring procedures is given in HSE guidance *Asbestos: exposure limits and measurement of airborne dust concentrations*[4] and *Asbestos fibres in air: sampling and evaluation by phase contrast microscopy (PCM) under the Control of Asbestos at Work Regulations*.[5]

Regulation 16   Health record

73   The health record should be kept for 40 years in a safe place and contain at least the following information:

(a)   surname, forenames, sex, date of birth, permanent address, postcode, National Insurance number;

(b)   a record of types of work carried out with asbestos and, where relevant, its location, with start and end dates and with average duration of exposure in hours per week;

(c)   a record of any work with asbestos prior to this employment; and

(d)   dates of medical examination.

74   Anyone who is exposed above the action level must have been medically examined within the previous two years. Employers will need to obtain certificates of examination, or copies, for any employees who state that they have been examined under regulation 16 within the previous two years. Employers must check with the previous employer or examining doctor that the certificates are genuine.

Regulation 17   Washing facilities

75   The type and extent of washing facilities provided should be related to the type and amount of exposure as indicated by the assessment carried out under regulation 5. Where exposure is low and infrequent, the facilities can be shared with other workers not working with asbestos. In other cases, separate facilities will be necessary.

76   Where wash-basins alone are not adequate, separate shower facilities should be provided. More information on the provision and use of hygiene facilities is given in HSE guidance *Provision, use and maintenance of hygiene facilities for work with asbestos insulation and coatings*.[13]

Part II Specific advice on controlling asbestos exposure during manufacturing processes

Regulation 5

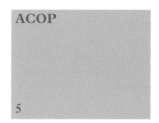

Assessing whether exposure can be prevented

77   Employers must first decide whether it is practicable to avoid exposure to asbestos altogether. In the manufacturing industry this must be by using a substitute material wherever practicable (see paragraph 79).

78   In addition to the requirements in paragraph 13, the assessment should explain why it is not possible to use a substitute material. Subsequent reviews of the assessment should take account of safer substitutes becoming available.

Regulation 8

Preventing exposure

Preventing exposure during manufacturing processes

79   Prevention of exposure must be the first objective. Employers must only use asbestos-containing products where using a less hazardous substitute is not practicable. When considering substitute materials for asbestos, employers should take into account all the potentially harmful properties of any proposed replacement, and balance against the possible benefits any new risks they might present to the health and safety of workers and others and to the environment. Where substitution is not practicable, employers must make sure that plant, processes and systems of work, including maintenance, are designed to prevent the release of asbestos into the air so far as is reasonably practicable. Further guidance on the safety of substitutes may be found in the guidance leaflet *Substitutes for chrysotile (white) asbestos*.[14]

Regulation 9

Reducing exposure

80   Where it is not practicable to prevent exposure, employers must reduce it to the lowest level reasonably practicable by means other than the use of respiratory protective equipment (RPE). This means keeping to an absolute minimum the amount of dust created during work with asbestos.

Reducing exposure in manufacturing processes

81   Technical measures to reduce exposure include local exhaust ventilation (LEV), made as effective as possible by enclosing the source of fibres where practicable. It is better to avoid fibre release than to create it and then have to remove it. In addition to any technical controls, employers should choose work methods which:

(a)   keep the quantity of asbestos used in each case to the minimum reasonably practicable;

(b)   limit the number of people exposed to the lowest possible number;

(c)   make sure that waste or debris is collected and removed by a dustless method from the work area as soon as possible in suitable labelled packages or containers;

(d)   make sure that damaged containers of raw fibre or waste are immediately repaired or placed inside another suitable container;

(e)   avoid the transfer of raw fibre to smaller containers;

(f)   avoid manual handling of raw fibre or intermediate products;

(g)   provide for intermediate and/or final cleaning or sealing of products;

(h)   make sure the premises and plant are kept clean;

(i)   have emergency procedures in place to deal with spillages or accidental releases of dust.

Maintenance of control measures

Maintenance of local exhaust ventilation in the manufacturing industry

82   Employers should make sure that where reasonably practicable, LEV is fitted with a device (eg a pressure gauge or airflow sensor) that can be easily seen, to check that the airflow through the system is being maintained. At installation the performance of the system should be thoroughly inspected to make sure that it works to its design specification. Subsequently, its condition and performance should be checked during each shift, inspected weekly and tested and thoroughly examined every six months. Defects in the system should be reported and made good as soon as possible. Where a defect may result in exposures above the relevant control limit, the work should be stopped until the defect is repaired. If a defect results in expected limits being exceeded, the same action should be taken.

Initial inspection

83   When a system is new, or has been substantially altered, it should be subject to a thorough inspection. This examination will establish that the system is operating to the design specification (within acceptable tolerance limits) and provide a base against which future measurements can be compared, and should include the following:

(a)   measurement of pressure and air velocities in the system, including:

    (i)   static pressure (velocity pressures can be calculated from point (iii)) behind captor hoods, or in multi-hood systems, at a representative sample of hoods (for an initial check it needs to be all hoods to ensure each is working to the required standard);

    (ii)   face velocities at captor hoods;

    (iii)   duct velocities as appropriate; and

    (iv)   static pressure differences across all fans and filters in the system;

(b)   qualitative checks of dust collection. These should include the use of a dust lamp to check the effectiveness of the LEV in collecting the dust. Smoke tubes can also be used to identify leaks in the system;

(c)   confirmation that the system is effectively controlling exposure; this should include appropriate measurement of airborne asbestos.

Shift check

84   The shift check should be carried out to make sure that the system responds when switched on, that gauges, if fitted, are within specified ranges, and that there is air movement.

Weekly inspection

85   LEV equipment will need to be inspected weekly when in use. This inspection should preferably be undertaken by someone other than the machine operator, eg a supervisor. This inspection should make sure that the equipment is checked for outward signs of damage, wear and tear and malfunction.

86   The inspection should include:

(a)   a visual check of:

   (i)   the position of hoods, etc, in relation to the dust source;

   (ii)   the condition of exhaust hoods, ductwork and dust collectors;

   (iii) any other outward signs that the system is not working properly, such as deposits of dust around the source;

(b)   a reading from any pressure gauge or airflow sensor to confirm that the system is working within the specified range, or, where no suitable gauge is fitted, a simple test such as a smoke tube.

Six-monthly examination and test

87   This examination should include:

(a)   a visual check of the outside of the system for deterioration or leakage;

(b)   a thorough examination of the fan, motor, filter housing or dust collection system to identify the need for planned preventative maintenance;

(c)   confirmation that the arrangement and method of use of the system remain satisfactory;

(d)   measurement of pressures and velocities as in paragraph 83(a); and

(e)   a check for escaping dust with a dust lamp as in paragraph 83(b).

88   Procedures for remedying defects should include provision for replacement, repair and remedial action within specified time limits.

Competency to carry out examinations and tests on exhaust ventilation

89   To be competent, those people carrying out examinations and tests on exhaust ventilation should have adequate knowledge, training and experience in examination methods and techniques. They should also be trained in the correct use of the various instruments and in the design and operation of the exhaust ventilation system so they can interpret their observations and results in relation to the design performance of the systems. They should be able to judge the extent to which they need help from other specialists if they are not able to carry out all parts of the examination themselves.

Regulation 13   Cleaning

Cleaning during manufacturing processes

90   Cleaning should be carried out as often as necessary to ensure that premises and plant are kept clean from all visible signs of dust - both asbestos and non-asbestos - which may have become contaminated. In particular, floors and workbenches, external plant surfaces, and washing and changing facilities should be cleaned at least once a day.

91   Walls and ceilings should be cleaned at least once a year. Overhead ledges and places where dust might gather should be cleaned as often as necessary to prevent the accumulation of asbestos.

92   Where it is reasonably practicable to do so, a fixed vacuum-cleaning system should be used. A fixed system should:

(a)   reach all areas to be cleaned;

(b)   have enough equipment for a number of vacuum outlets to be used at any one time;

(c)   provide adequate suction from each outlet when in use and cut off automatically when not in use;

(d)   whenever reasonably practicable, vent to the atmosphere; and

(e)   have HEPA filters.

93   If mobile vacuum cleaners are used, they should be of type H (BS 5415).[10]

94   If vacuum cleaners are not used, surfaces should be hosed or washed down, provided that residues are properly disposed of as hazardous waste. Small amounts of asbestos can be removed with a well-damped cloth, which should then be placed in a suitable container and sealed before it dries out. Dry manual brushing or sweeping must not be used to remove asbestos.

95   Buildings should be designed with smooth impervious walls, ceilings and surfaces and easy and safe access to overhead plant fixtures so that they can be effectively cleaned.

Regulation 18   Storage of waste and raw asbestos

96   Waste containers should be designed, constructed and maintained to prevent asbestos escaping during normal handling. For raw fibre or loose fibrous or dusty waste, or other asbestos waste in small fragments, double plastic sacks are suitable, provided they are unlikely to split during normal use. The inner sack should not be overfilled and each sack should be securely tied or sealed. Air should be pushed from the bag as far as possible before sealing. This activity should be carried out carefully, in a designated area, with LEV and PPE, because the air exhausted from the bags may be contaminated with asbestos. Stronger containers are necessary if the waste contains sharp objects which could puncture a plastic bag.

Regulation 4

Identifying asbestos before starting work with building materials liable to contain asbestos

ACOP

97   Where employers are about to start work on building materials which may contain asbestos, they should first either:

(a)   check whether the material does contain asbestos, and if so the type, by having it analysed; or

(b)   assume that the material contains the most hazardous types of asbestos, crocidolite (blue) or amosite (brown) and take the precautions outlined in either this Approved Code of Practice (ACOP) or the ACOP *Work with asbestos insulation, asbestos coating and asbestos insulating board.*[2]

98   Any information on the type of asbestos and the results of any analysis should be covered in the assessment required by regulation 5.

4

Regulation 5

Assessing whether exposure can be prevented

ACOP

99   Employers must first decide whether it is practicable to avoid exposure to asbestos altogether. As far as building work is concerned, employers must, as far as is reasonably practicable, avoid disturbing asbestos materials, by carrying out the work in a different way.

When to carry out an assessment

100   It is not always necessary to make an assessment before each individual job. Where an employer carries out work which involves very similar jobs on a number of sites on the same type of asbestos material, eg electrical and plumbing jobs, only one assessment for that work may be needed. However, where the degree and nature of the work varies significantly from site to site, for example in demolition or construction, or the type of asbestos materials vary, a new assessment and plan of work will be necessary.

5

Regulation 5A

Plan of work (or method statement) for work involving building materials containing asbestos

ACOP

101   For certain work involving asbestos, such as demolition, construction work or work on removing asbestos or asbestos-containing products from buildings, structures, installations or ships, a plan of work should be drawn up before work of any kind begins. Employers must follow the plan of work as far as it is reasonably practicable to do so. Where unacceptable risks to health and/or safety are discovered while work is in progress, work should be stopped until a new plan of work is drawn up, or the existing plan is amended.

102   This new plan should specify that, so far as is reasonably practicable, asbestos and/or asbestos-containing products are removed before demolition or major refurbishment begins. The plan of work, sometimes called the method statement, should cover the following information:

5A

(a)   the nature and likely duration of the work;

(b) the address and location where the work is to be carried out;

(c) the methods to be used where the work involves the handling of asbestos or of material containing asbestos;

(d) the type of equipment, including personal protective equipment, used for:

  (i) the protection and decontamination of those carrying out the work;

  (ii) the protection of other people present on or near the worksite.

103 If requested, the plan of work must be notified to the appropriate enforcing authority before the start of the work.

104 A copy of the plan of work should be kept readily available on site and should be brought to the attention of anyone checking the cleanliness of the site by visual inspection and air clearance monitoring; this also applies to anyone carrying out such monitoring once the work has come to an end. Employers should make a copy of the plan of work available on request to employees, employee representatives and to safety representatives.

Preventing and controlling exposure

Preventing exposure during work with asbestos-containing building materials

105 Employers must only carry out work which disturbs building materials containing asbestos when there is no other reasonably practicable way of doing the work.

Reducing exposure during work with asbestos-containing building materials

106 When work is carried out with asbestos materials or which is likely to disturb asbestos materials in buildings or other structures (machinery, vessels, vehicles or plant), employers must reduce employees' exposure and the exposure of others affected by the work as far as is reasonably practicable by:

(a) removing materials containing asbestos before any other major work begins, using methods which keep dust levels to a minimum;

(b) limiting the number of people exposed to the lowest possible number;

(c) using work methods which avoid creating dust, eg by removing sheets whole or using a wrap-and-cut method and avoiding the use of power tools, keeping materials thoroughly wet, utilising local exhaust ventilation (LEV) systems such as cowls on drills and shadow vacuuming;

(d) avoiding dry work methods such as abrasion, sanding, machining or cutting of asbestos materials;

(e) segregation by not carrying out asbestos work and other work in the same place at the same time; and

(f) keeping the work area clean by clearing up using methods which do not spread asbestos dust before waste debris and dust accumulate.

Regulation 10   Maintenance of control measures

Maintenance and testing of vacuum cleaners

107 Vacuum-cleaning equipment should be used during or after maintenance and repair work on building materials which contain asbestos. Employers should make sure that vacuum-cleaning equipment, type H (BS 5415),[10] is inspected weekly when in use and tested and examined thoroughly every six months in accordance with the manufacturer's instructions. Before the vacuum cleaner is used, employers should ensure that their employees check to see whether the waste bag needs to be emptied and to see that the vacuum is providing adequate suction. This needs to be done in a designated area by workers using PPE because of the potential for fibres to be released.

Regulation 13   Cleanliness of premises and plant

Cleaning during and after work with building materials containing asbestos

108 Employers should make sure that employees clean up asbestos debris and dust as they work, rather than let it accumulate. Dustless methods should be used, either a type H (BS 5415) vacuum cleaner or damp cloths, for small amounts of asbestos dust. Dry manual brushing or sweeping must not be used to remove asbestos dust.

109 When work with asbestos comes to an end in a workplace or when a contractor has carried out repair or maintenance work, or when an unforeseen escape of asbestos dust has occurred, the work area should be thoroughly cleaned before being handed over for reoccupation. All visible traces of asbestos dust and debris should be removed and a thorough visual inspection carried out.

Regulation 18   Storage of waste asbestos

110 Waste containers should be designed, constructed and maintained to prevent any of the asbestos escaping during normal handling. For loose fibrous or dusty waste, or other asbestos waste in small fragments, double plastic sacks are suitable, provided they are unlikely to split during normal use. The inner sack should not be overfilled and each sack should be securely tied or sealed. Air should be pushed from the sack as far as possible before sealing. Precautions will need to be taken as the exhaust air may be contaminated. Stronger containers are necessary if the waste contains sharp objects which could puncture a plastic bag.

111 Wherever practicable, large pieces of rigid material must not be broken or cut for disposal in plastic sacks. They should be double-wrapped intact in sheet plastic or other suitable material, or placed in a sealed container such as a lockable skip. If an open skip is used it should be tightly and securely sheeted with tarpaulin or a similar strong material.

Regulations

The Control of Asbestos at Work Regulations printed to include all the amendments made since they came into force. The Control of Asbestos at Work Regulations 1987 (SI 1987 No 2115), as amended by the Control of Asbestos at Work (Amendment) Regulations 1992 (SI 1992 No 3068), and the Personal Protective Equipment at Work Regulations 1992 (SI 1992 No 2966) and the Control of Asbestos at Work (Amendment) Regulations 1998 (SI 1998 No 3235).

Arrangement of Regulations

Regulation 1

Regulation
1

Citation and commencement

These Regulations may be cited as the Control of Asbestos at Work Regulations 1987 and shall come into force on 1 March 1988.

Regulation 2

Regulation

Interpretation

(1)   In these Regulations, unless the context otherwise requires -

"action level" means one of the following cumulative exposures to asbestos over a continuous 12-week period when measured or calculated by a method approved by the Health and Safety Commission, namely -

(a)   where the exposure is solely to chrysotile, 72 fibre-hours per millilitre of air; or

(b)   where exposure is to any other form of asbestos either alone or in mixtures including mixtures of chrysotile with any other form of asbestos, 48 fibre-hours per millilitre of air; or

(c)   where both types of exposure occur separately during the 12-week period concerned, a proportionate number of fibre-hours per millilitre of air.

"adequate" means adequate having regard only to the nature and degree of exposure to asbestos and "adequately" shall be construed accordingly;

"approved" means approved for the time being in writing by the Health and Safety Commission or the Health and Safety Executive as the case may be;

"asbestos" means any of the following minerals, that is to say, crocidolite, amosite, chrysotile, fibrous actinolite, fibrous anthophyllite, fibrous tremolite and any mixture containing any of those minerals;

"asbestos area" and "respirator zone" shall be construed in accordance with regulation 14;

"control limit" means one of the following concentrations of asbestos in the atmosphere when measured or calculated by a method approved by the Health and Safety Commission, namely -

(a)   for chrysotile -

(i)   0.3 fibres per millilitre of air averaged over any continuous period of 4 hours;

(ii)   0.9 fibres per millilitre of air average over any continuous period of 10 minutes;

(b)   for any other form of asbestos either alone or in mixtures including mixtures of chrysotile with any other form of asbestos -

(i)   0. 2 fibres per millilitre of air averaged over any continuous period of 4 hours;

(ii)   0.6 fibres per millilitre of air averaged over any continuous period of 10 minutes;

"EN 45001" means European Standard EN 45001, "General criteria for the operation of testing laboratories" accepted by the Comité Européen de Normalisation and the Comité Européen de Normalisation Electrotechnique (CEN/CENELEC) on 23rd June 1989[a], as revised or reissued from time to time;

"the Executive" means the Health and Safety Executive.

(2) For the purposes of these Regulations, except as specified in regulation 8(2), in determining whether an employee is exposed to asbestos or whether the extent of such exposure exceeds the action level or any control limit, no account shall be taken of any respiratory protective equipment which, for the time being, is being worn by that employee.

(3) In these Regulations, unless the context otherwise requires -

(a) a reference to a numbered regulation or Schedule is a reference to the regulation or Schedule in these Regulations so numbered; and

(b) a reference to a numbered paragraph is a reference to the paragraph so numbered in the regulation or Schedule in which that reference appears.

(a) Reference number EN 45001: 1989 E.

Regulation 3

Duties under these Regulations

(1) Where any duty is placed by these Regulations on an employer in respect of his employees, he shall, so far as is reasonably practicable, be under a like duty in respect of any other person who may be affected by the work activity, whether at work or not, except that the duties of the employer -

(a) under regulation 7 (information, instruction and training) shall not extend to persons who are not his employees unless those persons are on the premises where the work is being carried out; and

(b) under regulation 16 (health records and medical surveillance) shall not extend to persons who are not his employees.

(2) These Regulations shall apply to a self-employed person as they apply to an employer and an employee and as if that self-employed person were both an employer and an employee.

(3) Nothing in these Regulations shall prejudice any requirement imposed by or under any enactment relating to public health or the protection of the environment.

(4) Regulation 13(1), insofar as it requires an employer to ensure that premises are thoroughly cleaned, shall not apply to -

(a) a fire authority in respect of premises attended, for the purpose of fighting a fire or in an emergency, by a fire brigade maintained by that authority; or

(b) the employer of persons who attend a ship in dock premises for the purpose of fighting a fire or in an emergency, in respect of any ship so attended,

and in this regulation, "ship" includes all vessels and hovercraft which operate on water or land and water, and "dock premises" means any dock, wharf, quay, jetty or other place at which ships load or unload goods or embark or disembark passengers, together with neighbouring land or water which is used or occupied, or intended to be used or occupied, for those or incidental activities, and any part of a ship when used for those or incidental activities.

Regulation 4

Identification of the type of asbestos

An employer shall not carry out any work which exposes or is liable to expose any of his employees to asbestos unless either -

(a)   before commencing that work, he has identified, by analysis or otherwise, the type of asbestos involved in the work; or

(b)   he has assumed that the asbestos is not chrysotile alone and for the purposes of these Regulations has treated it accordingly.

Regulation 5

Assessment of work which exposes employees to asbestos

(1)   Subject to paragraph (3), an employer shall not carry out any work which exposes or is liable to expose any of his employees to asbestos unless he has made an adequate assessment of that exposure.

(2)   Without prejudice to the generality of paragraph (1), that assessment shall -

(a)   subject to regulation 4, identify the type of asbestos to which employees are liable to be exposed;

(b)   determine the nature and degree of exposure which may occur in the course of the work; and

(c)   set out the steps to be taken to prevent or reduce to the lowest level reasonably practicable that exposure.

(3)   Where work which exposed or was liable to expose employees to asbestos had been commenced before the coming into force of these Regulations or within 28 days after that date, it shall be sufficient compliance with paragraph (1) if the employer makes the assessment required by that paragraph within 28 days after the date of coming into force of these Regulations.

(4)   The assessment required by paragraph (1) shall be reviewed regularly and a new assessment substituted when -

(a)   there is reason to suspect that the existing assessment is no longer valid; or

(b)   there is a significant change in the work to which the assessment relates.

(5)   The employer shall keep a copy of any assessment required by paragraph (1) which is in writing at any place at which the work to which the assessment relates is being carried out and for any period during which the work to which the assessment relates is being carried out.

Regulation 5A

Plans of work

(1)   The employer shall not undertake any work with asbestos consisting of the removal of asbestos from any building, structure, plant, or installation or from a ship (including its demolition) unless he has prepared a suitable written plan of work detailing how the work is to be carried out and shall keep that plan at least until the date on which the work to which the plan relates has been completed.

(1A)   The employer shall keep a copy of the plan of work made in pursuance of paragraph (1) at any place at which the work to which the plan relates is being carried out and for any period during which the work to which the plan relates is being carried out.

(2)   The plan of work made in pursuance of paragraph (1) shall include in particular details of -

(a)   the nature and probable duration of the work;

(b)   the location of the place where the work is to be carried out;

(c)   the methods to be applied where the work involves the handling of asbestos or materials containing asbestos;

(d)   the characteristics of the equipment to be used for -

(i)   protection and decontamination of those carrying out the work,

(ii)   protection of other persons on or near the worksite.

(3)   The employer shall ensure, so far as is reasonably practicable, that the work to which the plan of work made in pursuance of paragraph (1) relates is carried out in accordance with that plan.

Regulation 6

Notification of work with asbestos

(1)   This regulation shall apply to any work in which an employee is or is liable to be exposed to asbestos unless -

(a)   the extent of that exposure neither exceeds nor is liable to exceed the action level; or

(b)   the employer is licensed under regulation 3(1) of the Asbestos (Licensing) Regulations 1983[a] to carry out the work and is doing so in accordance with the terms and conditions of that licence or is exempted by regulation 3(2)(b) of those Regulations from those requirements.

(2)   An employer shall not carry out any work to which this regulation applies for the first time unless he has notified the enforcing authority in writing of the particulars specified in Schedule 1 at least 14 days before commencing that work or before such shorter time as the enforcing authority may agree.

(3)   Where an employer has notified work in accordance with paragraph (2) and there is a material change in that work which might affect the particulars so notified (including the cessation of the work), the employer shall forthwith notify the enforcing authority of that change.

(a) SI 1983/1649.

(4) Where the work with asbestos was commenced before the date of coming into force of these Regulations or is commenced within 56 days after that date, it shall be sufficient compliance with paragraph (2) if the employer either -

(a) notifies the enforcing authority in accordance with paragraph (2) within 28 days after the coming into force of these Regulations; or

(b) had, before the revocation of regulation 6 of the Asbestos Regulations 1969[a] notified the enforcing authority in accordance with that regulation.

(a) SI 1969/690.

Regulation 7

Information, instruction and training

(1) Every employer shall ensure that adequate information, instruction and training is given to his employees -

(a) who are or are liable to be exposed to asbestos so that they are aware of the risks from asbestos and the precautions which should be observed;

(b) who carry out any work in connection with the employer's duties under these Regulations, so that they can carry out that work effectively.

(2) The information, instruction and training referred to in paragraph (1) shall be -

(a) given at suitable intervals; and

(b) adapted to take account of any significant changes in the type of work carried out or methods of work used by the employer.

Regulation 8

Prevention or reduction of exposure to asbestos

(1) Every employer shall -

(a) prevent the exposure of his employees to asbestos;

(b) where it is not reasonably practicable to prevent such exposure, reduce to the lowest level reasonably practicable the exposure of his employees to asbestos by measures other than the use of respiratory protective equipment.

(1A) Without prejudice to the generality of paragraph (1), where employees may be exposed to asbestos in any manufacturing process or in the installation of any product, prevention of such exposure shall be achieved, where it is practicable, by substituting for asbestos a substance which, under the conditions of its use, does not create a risk to the health of his employees or creates a lesser risk than that created by asbestos.

(2) Where, in pursuance of paragraph (1), it is not reasonably practicable to reduce the exposure of an employee to below both the control limits which apply to that exposure, then, in addition to taking the measures required by that paragraph, the employer shall provide that employee with suitable respiratory protective equipment which will reduce the concentration of asbestos in the air inhaled by the

employee (after taking into account the effect of that respiratory protective equipment) to a concentration which is as low as is reasonably practicable and in any event below those control limits.

(3) Respiratory protective equipment provided in pursuance of paragraph (2) shall comply with paragraph 3(A) or, where no requirement is imposed by that paragraph, shall conform to a standard approved in either case by the Executive for the purposes of this regulation.

(3A) Any respiratory protective equipment provided in pursuance of paragraph (2) or protective clothing provided in pursuance of regulation 11(1) shall comply with this paragraph if it complies with any enactment (whether in an Act or instrument) which implements in Great Britain any provision on design or manufacture with respect to health or safety in any relevant Community directive listed in Schedule 1 to the Personal Protective Equipment at Work Regulations 1992 which is applicable to that item of respiratory protective equipment or protective clothing.

(4) If an unforeseen event occurs which results in the escape of asbestos into the workplace at a concentration that is liable to exceed any applicable control limit, the employer shall ensure that -

(a) only those persons who are responsible for the carrying out of repairs and other necessary work are permitted in the affected area and that those persons are provided with appropriate respiratory protective equipment and protective clothing; and

(b) employees and other persons who may have been affected by the event are informed of it forthwith.

Regulation 9

Use of control measures etc

(1) Every employer who provides any control measure, personal protective equipment or other thing or facility pursuant to these Regulations shall ensure so far as is reasonably practicable that it is properly used or applied as the case may be.

(2) Every employee shall make full and proper use of any control measure, personal protective equipment or other thing or facility provided pursuant to these Regulations and if he discovers any defect therein he shall report it forthwith to his employer.

Regulation 10

Maintenance of control measures etc

(1) Every employer who provides any control measure, personal protective equipment or other thing or facility pursuant to these Regulations shall ensure that it is maintained in a clean and efficient state, in efficient working order, and in good repair, and in the case of exhaust ventilation equipment and respiratory protective equipment (except disposable respiratory protective equipment), is also regularly examined and tested at suitable intervals by a competent person.

(2) Every employer shall make a suitable record of work carried out in accordance with paragraph (1) which shall be kept for at least five years from the date on which it was made.

Regulation 11

Provision and cleaning of protective clothing

(1)   Every employer shall provide adequate and suitable protective clothing for such of his employees as are exposed or liable to be exposed to asbestos, unless no significant quantity of asbestos is liable to be deposited on the clothes of the employee while he is at work.

(2)   The employer shall ensure that any protective clothing provided in pursuance of paragraph (1) is either disposed of as asbestos waste or adequately cleaned at suitable intervals.

(3)   The cleaning required by paragraph (2) shall be carried out on the premises where the exposure to asbestos has occurred, where those premises are suitably equipped for such cleaning, or in a suitably equipped laundry and protective clothing which has been used and is to be removed from those premises (whether for cleaning, further use or disposal) shall, before being removed, be packed in a suitable container which shall be labelled in accordance with the provisions of Schedule 2 as if it were a product containing asbestos or, in the case of protective clothing intended for disposal as waste, in accordance with regulation 18(3).

(4)   Where, as a result of the failure or improper use of the protective clothing provided in pursuance of paragraph (1), a significant quantity of asbestos is deposited on the personal clothing of an employee, then, for the purposes of paragraphs (2) and (3) that personal clothing shall be treated as if it were protective clothing.

Regulation 12

Duty to prevent or reduce the spread of asbestos

Every employer shall prevent or, where this is not reasonably practicable, reduce to the lowest level reasonably practicable, the spread of asbestos from any place where work under his control is carried out.

Regulation 13

Cleanliness of premises and plant

(1)   Every employer who undertakes work which exposes or is liable to expose his employees to asbestos shall ensure that the premises or those parts of premises where that work is carried out and the plant used in connection with that work are kept in a clean state and, in particular, where such work has been completed the premises or those parts of the premises where the work was carried out are thoroughly cleaned.

(2)   Subject to paragraph (3), where a manufacturing process which gives rise to asbestos dust is carried out in a building, the employer shall ensure that any part of the building in which the process is carried out is -

(a)   so designed and constructed as to facilitate cleaning; and

(b)   is equipped with an adequate and suitable vacuum cleaning system which shall, where reasonably practicable, be a fixed system.

(3)   Paragraph (2) (a) shall not apply to any building in which, immediately before the coming into force of these Regulations, there was carried out a process to which either -

(a)   prior to its revocation regulation 13 of the Asbestos Regulations 1969 applied and the process was carried out in compliance with that regulation; or

(b)   that regulation did not apply.

Regulation 14

Designated areas

(1) Every employer shall ensure that any area in which work under his control is carried out is designated as -

(a) an asbestos area, where the exposure to asbestos of an employee who worked in that area for the whole of his working time would exceed or would be liable to exceed the action level;

(b) a respirator zone, where the concentration of asbestos in that area would exceed or would be liable to exceed any control limit.

(2) Asbestos areas and respirator zones shall be clearly and separately demarcated and identified by notices indicating -

(a) that the area is an asbestos area or a respirator zone or both, as the case may be; and

(b) in the case of a respirator zone, that the exposure of an employee who enters it is liable to exceed a control limit and, if it does, that respiratory protective equipment must be worn.

(3) The employer shall not permit any employee other than an employee who by reason of his work is required to be in an area designated in accordance with paragraph (1), to enter or remain in any such area and only employees who are so permitted shall enter or remain in any such area.

(4) Every employer shall take suitable steps to ensure that -

(a) his employees do not eat, drink or smoke in any area designated as an asbestos area or a respirator zone; and

(b) in such a case, arrangements are made for such employees to eat or drink in some other place.

Regulation 15

Air monitoring

(1) Every employer shall take adequate steps to monitor the exposure of his employees to asbestos where such monitoring is appropriate for the protection of the health of those employees.

(2) The employer shall keep a suitable record of any monitoring carried out in accordance with paragraph (1) and that record or a suitable summary thereof shall be kept -

(a) in a case where exposure is such that a health record is required to be kept under regulation 16, for at least 40 years;

(b) in any other case, for at least five years.

Regulation 15A

Compliance with EN 45001

(1) Every employer who carries out any measurement of the concentration of asbestos fibres present in the air, whether or not in pursuance of regulation 15(1), shall ensure that he meets criteria equivalent to those set out in paragraphs 5.1, 5.2, 5.3, 5.4.1 and 5.4.2 of EN 45001.

(2) Every employer who requests a laboratory to carry out any measurement of the concentration of asbestos fibres present in the air, whether or not in pursuance of regulation 15(1), shall ensure that that laboratory is accredited by an appropriate body as complying with EN 45001.

Regulation 16   Health records and medical surveillance

(1) Every employer shall ensure that a health record containing particulars approved by the Executive relating to each of his employees who is exposed to asbestos is maintained unless the exposure of that employee does not exceed the action level and that that record or a copy thereof is kept for at least 40 years from the date of the last entry made in it.

(2) Every employer shall ensure that each of his employees who is exposed to asbestos is under adequate medical surveillance by an employment medical adviser or appointed doctor unless the exposure of that employee does not exceed the action level, and such medical surveillance shall include -

(a) a medical examination not more than two years before the beginning of such exposure; and

(b) periodic medical examinations at intervals of not more than two years or such shorter time as the employment medical adviser or appointed doctor may require while such exposure continues, and

each such medical examination shall include a specific examination of the chest.

(3) Where an employee has been examined in accordance with paragraph (2), the employment medical adviser or appointed doctor shall issue to the employer and that employee a certificate stating that he has been so examined and the date of the examination and the employer shall keep that certificate or a copy thereof for at least four years from the date on which it was issued.

(4) An employee to whom this regulation applies shall, when required by his employer and at the cost of the employer, present himself during his working hours for such examination and tests as may be required for the purposes of paragraph (2) and shall furnish the employment medical adviser or appointed doctor with such information concerning his health as may reasonably be required.

(5) Where medical surveillance is carried out on the premises of the employer, the employer shall ensure that suitable facilities are made available for the purpose.

(6) On reasonable notice being given, the employer shall allow any of his employees access to the health record which relates to that employee.

(7) Where before the coming into force of these Regulations, an employee was engaged in work in which he was exposed to asbestos to an extent which exceeds the action level and continues to be engaged in such work, it shall be a sufficient compliance with paragraph (2) if either -

(a) he is medically examined within six months after the date of coming into force of these Regulations; or

(b) in a case where -

(i) he had been medically examined before the date of coming into force of these Regulations, and

(ii) that examination was for the purpose of regulation 6 of the Asbestos (Licensing) Regulations 1983 or an employment medical adviser or appointed doctor has certified that it is appropriate for the examination to be deemed to be an examination for the purposes of paragraph (2)(a),

he is next examined within two years after the date of that examination or within such shorter time as the employment medical adviser or appointed doctor may require.

(8)(a)Fees shall be payable in accordance with the following provisions of this paragraph to the Health and Safety Executive in respect of a medical examination for the purposes of this regulation by an employment medical adviser.

(b)   The fees shall be payable in the case of the examination of an employee, by his employer; and, in the case of the examination of a self-employed person, by that self-employed person.

(c)   The fees shall be a basic fee of £34.50 for each examination, together with an additional fee of £27.00 in respect of all X-rays taken in connection with any one examination, and of £15.50 in respect of all laboratory tests carried out in respect of any one examination.

(9)   In this Regulation -

"appointed doctor" means a registered medical practitioner who is for the time being appointed in writing by the Executive for the purposes of this regulation;

"employment medical adviser" means an employment medical adviser appointed under section 56(1) of the Health and Safety at Work etc. Act 1974[a];

"medical examination", except in paragraph (8), includes any laboratory tests and X-rays that the employment medical adviser or appointed doctor may require.

16

(a) 1974 c37.

Regulation 17

Washing and changing facilities

(1)   Every employer shall ensure that, for any of his employees who is exposed or liable to be exposed to asbestos, adequate and suitable -

(a)   washing and changing facilities;

(b)   where he is required to provide protective clothing, facilities for the storage of -

(i)   that protective clothing, and

(ii)   personal clothing not worn during work hours;

(c)   where he is required to provide respiratory protective equipment, facilities for the storage of that equipment are provided.

(2)   The facilities provided under paragraph (1) for the storage of personal protective clothing, of personal clothing not worn during working hours and of respiratory protective equipment shall be separate from each other.

17

Regulation 18

Storage, distribution and labelling of raw asbestos and asbestos waste

Regulation

18

(1)   Every employer who undertakes work with asbestos shall ensure that any raw asbestos or waste which contains asbestos is not -

(a)   stored;

(b)   received into or despatched from any place of work; or

(c)   distributed, except in a totally enclosed distribution system, within any place of work,

unless it is in a suitable and sealed container clearly marked in accordance with paragraphs (2) and (3) showing that it contains asbestos.

(2)   Raw asbestos shall be labelled in accordance with the provisions of Schedule 2.

(3)   Waste containing asbestos shall be labelled -

(a)   where the Carriage of Dangerous Goods (Classification, Packaging and Labelling) and Use of Transportable Pressure Receptacles Regulations 1996[(a)] apply, in accordance with those Regulations;

(b)   where the waste is conveyed by road in a road tanker or tank container in circumstances where the Carriage of Dangerous Goods by Road Regulations 1996[(b)] apply, in accordance with those Regulations;

(c)   in any other case, in accordance with the provisions of Schedule 2.

(a) SI 1996/2092.
(b) SI 1996/2095.

Regulation 19

Supply of products containing asbestos for use at work

Regulation

19

(1)   Subject to paragraph (2), a person shall not supply any product which contains asbestos, being an article or substance for use at work, unless that product is labelled in accordance with the provisions of Schedule 2.

(2)   Where a product contains a component containing asbestos it shall be sufficient compliance with this regulation if such component is labelled in accordance with the provisions of Schedule 2 except that where the size of such a component makes it impossible for a label to be fixed to the component neither the component nor the product need be labelled.

Regulation 20

Exemption certificates

Regulation

20

(1)   Subject to paragraph (2) of this regulation, the Executive may, by a certificate in writing, exempt any person or class of persons from all or any of the requirements or prohibitions imposed by these Regulations and any such exemption may be granted subject to conditions and to a limit of time and may be revoked by a certificate in writing at any time.

(2) The Executive shall not grant any such exemption unless having regard to the circumstances of the case and in particular to -

(a)   the conditions, if any, which it proposes to attach to the exemption; and

(b)   any other requirements imposed by or under any enactments which apply to the case,

it is satisfied that the health and safety of persons who are likely to be affected by the exemption will not be prejudiced in consequence of it and that any provision imposed by the European Communities in respect of the encouragement of improvements in the safety and health of workers at work will be satisfied.

Regulation 21

Extension outside Great Britain

These Regulations shall apply to any work outside Great Britain which sections 1 to 59 and 80 to 82 of the Health and Safety at Work etc. Act 1974[(a)] apply by virtue of the Health and Safety at Work etc. Act 1974 (Application outside Great Britain) Order 1989[(b)] as they apply to work in Great Britain.

(a) 1974 c.37.
(b) SI 1989/840.

Regulation 21A

Defence in proceedings for contravention of these Regulations

In any proceedings for an offence consisting of a contravention of these Regulations it shall be a defence for any person to provide that he took all reasonable precautions and exercised all due diligence to avoid the commission of that offence.

Regulation 22

Revocations and savings

(1)   The Asbestos Regulations 1969[(a)] are revoked.

(2)   Regulation 6 of the Asbestos (Licensing) Regulations 1983[(b)] is revoked.

(3)   Any report required to be kept under regulation 7(4) of the Asbestos Regulations 1969 or certificate required to be kept under regulation 6 of the Asbestos (Licensing) Regulations 1983 shall, notwithstanding the revocation of those Regulations, be kept in the same manner and for the same period as if the revocations mentioned in paragraphs (2) and (3) had not taken effect.

(a) SI 1969/960.
(b) SI 1983/1649.

Schedule 1   Particulars to be included in a notification

Regulation 6(2)

1   The following particulars are to be included in a notification made in accordance with regulation 6(2), namely -

(a)   the name, address and telephone number of -

    (i)   the notifier, and

    (ii)   his usual place of business;

(b)   a brief description of -

    (i)   the type(s) of asbestos used or handled (crocidolite, amosite, chrysotile or other), and

    (ii)   maximum quantity of asbestos held on the premises at any one time, and

    (iii)   the activities or processes involved, and

    (iv)   the products manufactured (where applicable);

(c)   date of commencement of the work activity where work has yet to begin.

Schedule 2

The labelling of raw asbestos, asbestos waste and products containing asbestos

Regulation 18(2) and (3) and 19

1   (1)   Subject to sub-paragraphs (2) and (3) of this paragraph, the label to be used on -

(a)   raw asbestos (together with the labelling required under the Chemicals Hazard Information and Packaging for Supply Regulations 1994, SI 1994/3247) and the Carriage of Dangerous Goods (Classification, Packaging and Labelling) and Use of Transportable Pressure Receptacles Regulations 1996, SI 1996/2092;

(b)   asbestos waste (when required to be so labelled by regulation 18(3)); and

(c)   products containing asbestos (including used protective clothing to which regulation 11(2) applies),

shall be in the form and in the colours of the following diagram and shall comply with the specifications set out in paragraphs 2 and 3.

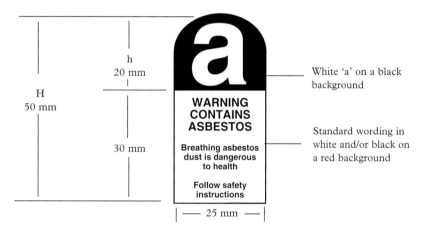

(2)   In the case of any product containing crocidolite, the words "contains asbestos" shown in the diagram shall be replaced by the words "contains crocidolite/blue asbestos".

(3)   Where the label is printed directly onto a product a single colour contrasting with the background colour may be used.

2   The dimensions in millimetres of the label shall be those shown on the diagram, except that larger measurements may be used, but in that case the dimension of the label indicated as h, on the diagram in paragraph 1(1) above, shall be 40% of the dimension indicated as H on that diagram.

3   The label shall be clearly and indelibly printed so that the words in the lower half of the label can be easily read, and those words shall be printed in black or white.

4   (1)   Without prejudice to the provisions of any other legislation relating to health and safety at work, where any product may undergo processing or finishing it shall bear a label containing any safety instructions appropriate to the particular product and in particular the following instructions -

"operate if possible out of doors or in a well ventilated place";

"preferably use hand tools or low speed tools equipped, if necessary, with an appropriate dust extraction facility. If high speed tools are used, they should always be so equipped";

"if possible, dampen before cutting or drilling";

"dampen dust and place it in a properly closed receptacle and dispose of it safely".

(2)   Any additional safety information given on any label shall not detract from or contradict the safety information given in accordance with sub-paragraph (1) above.

5   (1)   Labelling of packaged and unpackaged products in accordance with the foregoing paragraphs shall be effected by means of -

    (a)   an adhesive label firmly affixed to the product or its packaging, as the case may be;

    (b)   a tie-on label firmly attached to the product or its packaging, as the case may be; or

    (c)   direct printing onto the product or its packaging, as the case may be.

(2)   Where, in the case of an unpackaged product, it is not reasonably practicable to comply with the provisions of sub-paragraph (1) above the label shall be printed on a suitable sheet accompanying the product.

(3)   Labelling of raw asbestos and asbestos waste shall be effected in accordance with sub-paragraphs (1)(a) or (c) above.

(4)   For the purposes of this Schedule, a product supplied in loose plastic or other similar wrapping (including plastic and paper bags) but no other packaging, shall be treated as being supplied in a package whether the product is placed in such wrapping at the time of its supply or was already so wrapped before that time. But no wrapping in which a product is placed at the time of its supply shall be regarded as packaging if any product contained in it is labelled in accordance with the requirements of this Schedule or any other packaging in which that product is contained is so labelled.

References

1   *The Asbestos (Licensing) Regulations 1983* SI 1983/1649 HMSO 1983 ISBN 0 11 037649 8 as amended by the *Asbestos (Licensing) (Amendment) Regulations 1998* SI 1998/3233 The Stationery Office 1999 ISBN 0 11 080279 9

2   *Work with asbestos insulation, asbestos coating and asbestos insulating board. Control of Asbestos at Work Regulations 1987. Approved Code of Practice* (Third edition) L28 HSE Books 1999 ISBN 0 7176 1674 6

3   *Health and Safety at Work etc Act 1974* HMSO 1974 ISBN 0 10 543774 3

4   *Asbestos: Exposure limits and measurement of airborne dust concentrations* EH10 HSE Books 2001 ISBN 0 7176 2129 4

5   *Asbestos fibre in air: Sampling and evaluation by phase contrast microscopy (PCM) under the Control of Asbestos at Work Regulations* MDHS39/4 HSE Books 1995 ISBN 0 7176 1113 2

6   *Control of Substances Hazardous to Health Regulations 1994* SI 1994/3246 HMSO 1994 ISBN 0 11 043721 7

7   *Training operatives and supervisors for work with asbestos insulation, asbestos coatings and asbestos insulating board* EH50 HSE Books 1988 ISBN 0 11 885400 3

8   *The Safety Representatives and Safety Committees Regulations 1977* SI 1977/500 HMSO 1977 ISBN 0 11 070500 9

9   *Health and Safety (Consultation with Employees) Regulations 1996* SI 1996/1513 HMSO 1996 ISBN 0 11 054839 6

10   British Standards Institution BS 5415: 1986 *Safety of electrical motor-operated industrial and commercial cleaning appliances*

11   *Monitoring strategies for toxic substances* HSG173 HSE Books 1997 ISBN 0 7176 1411 5

12   British Standards Institution EN 45001: 1989 *General criteria for the operation of testing laboratories*

13   *Provision, use and maintenance of hygiene facilities for work with asbestos insulation and coatings* EH47 HSE Books 1990 ISBN 0 11 885567 0

14   *Substitutes for chrysotile (white) asbestos* MISC155 HSE Books 1998 (Out of print)

Further reading

Asbestos (Prohibitions) Regulations 1992 SI 1992/3067 HMSO 1992 ISBN 0 11 025740 5

Special Waste Regulations 1996 SI 1996/972 HMSO 1996 ISBN 0 11 062941 8

Carriage of Dangerous Goods (Classification, Packaging and Labelling) and Use of Transportable Pressure Receptacles Regulations 1996 SI 1996/2092 HMSO 1996 ISBN 0 11 062923 X

Carriage of Dangerous Goods by Road Regulations 1996 SI 1996/2095 HMSO 1996 ISBN 0 11 062926 4

Carriage of Dangerous Goods by Rail Regulations 1996 SI 1996/2089 HMSO 1996 ISBN 0 11 062919 1

Personal Protective Equipment at Work Regulations 1992 SI 1992/2966 HMSO 1992 ISBN 0 11 025832 0

Workplace (Health, Safety and Welfare) Regulations 1992 SI 1992/3004 HMSO 1992 ISBN 0 11 025804 5

Construction (Design and Management) Regulations 1994 SI 1994/3140 HMSO 1994 ISBN 0 11 043845 0

The Chemicals (Hazard Information and Packaging for Supply) Regulations 1994 SI 1994/3247 HMSO 1994 ISBN 0 11 043877 9 (as amended)

Working with asbestos cement HSG189/2 HSE Books 1999 ISBN 0 7176 1667 3

Managing asbestos in workplace premises INDG223(rev2) HSE Books 2001 (single copy free or priced packs of 10 ISBN 0 7176 2092 1)

Asbestos alert for building maintenance, repair and refurbishment workers Pocket card INDG188 HSE Books 1995 (single copy free or priced packs of 25 ISBN 0 7176 1209 0)

Asbestos dust kills: Keep your mask on INDG255(rev1) HSE Books 1999 (single copy free or priced packs of 20 ISBN 0 7176 1696 7)

Asbestos: Medical guidance note 1999 ISBN 0 7176 2417 X

While every effort has been made to ensure the accuracy of the references listed in this publication, their future availability cannot be guaranteed.

British Standards are available from BSI Customer Services, 389 Chiswick High Road, London W4 4AL Tel: 020 8996 9001 Fax: 020 8996 7001 Website: www.bsi-global.com

The Stationery Office (formerly HMSO) publications are available from The Publications Centre, PO Box 276, London SW8 5DT Tel: 0870 600 5522 Fax: 0870 600 5533 Website: www.clicktso.com (They are also available from bookshops.)

Printed and published by the Health and Safety Executive   C10   12/01